KEEP CALM AND COLOUR CACTI

summersdale

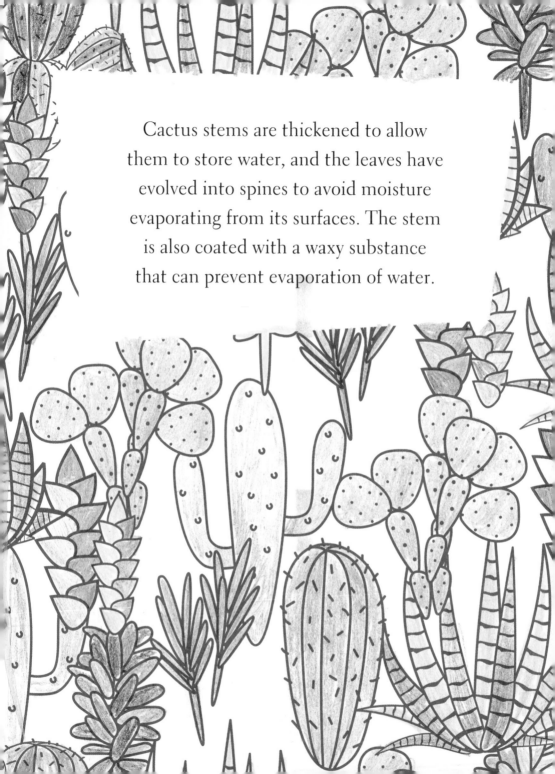

Cactus stems are thickened to allow
them to store water, and the leaves have
evolved into spines to avoid moisture
evaporating from its surfaces. The stem
is also coated with a waxy substance
that can prevent evaporation of water.

Bigger cacti can be used as
wood, much like trees.

In Mexico, they're felled for
building walls and roofs.

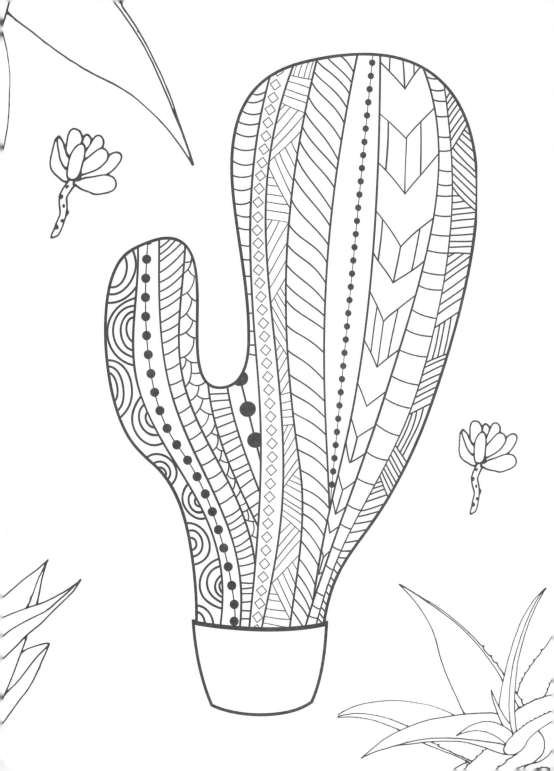

In the wild, the most important
factors for growth are water and
temperature. Deserts are very cold
at night but cacti survive – however,
if there's a frost they will die.

Reaching lifetimes of around
300 years, the Cardón cactus has the
longest lifespan of the cactus family.

The Saguaro cactus, the one most linked
with Western films and South America,
can grow more than 21 metres tall.

Although cactus spines can be an irritant to the skin or painful if ingested, they are not known to be poisonous.

It's not all sweetness: some cactus
flowers smell of rotten meat, which
might sound disgusting but acts
as a way of attracting insects.

The trunks of some cacti are
sometimes used to make a
type of Argentinian drum
called a *bombo legüero*.

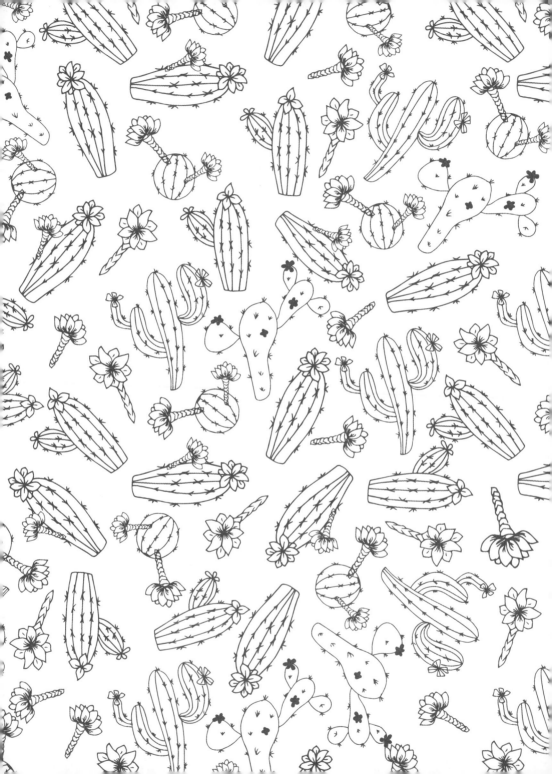

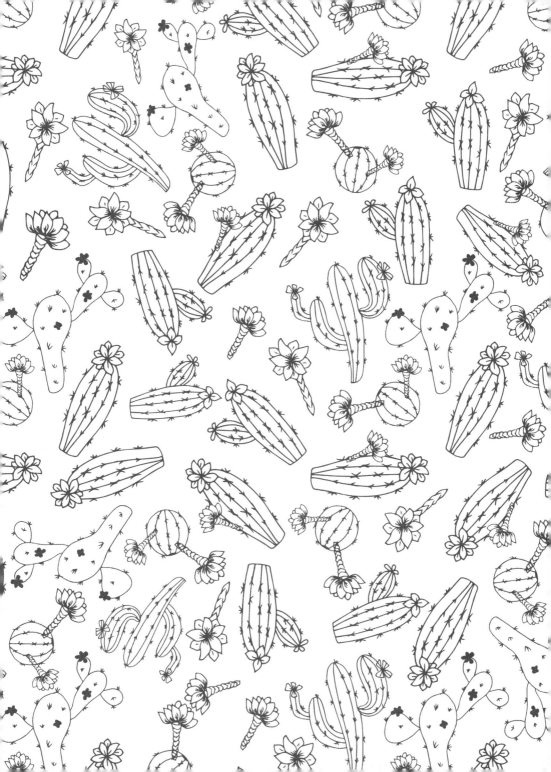

In Mexico, the roots of the
Peyote cactus were chewed by
Aztecs for their hallucinogenic
properties. Later on in history they
were used as an anaesthetic.

The fruit of some cactus
species can be eaten. Prickly
pears come from the *Opuntia
phaeacantha* cactus.

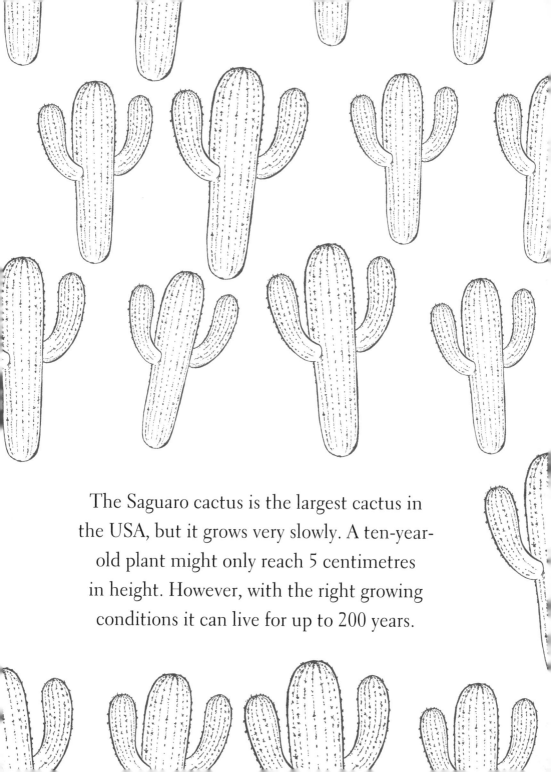

The Saguaro cactus is the largest cactus in the USA, but it grows very slowly. A ten-year-old plant might only reach 5 centimetres in height. However, with the right growing conditions it can live for up to 200 years.

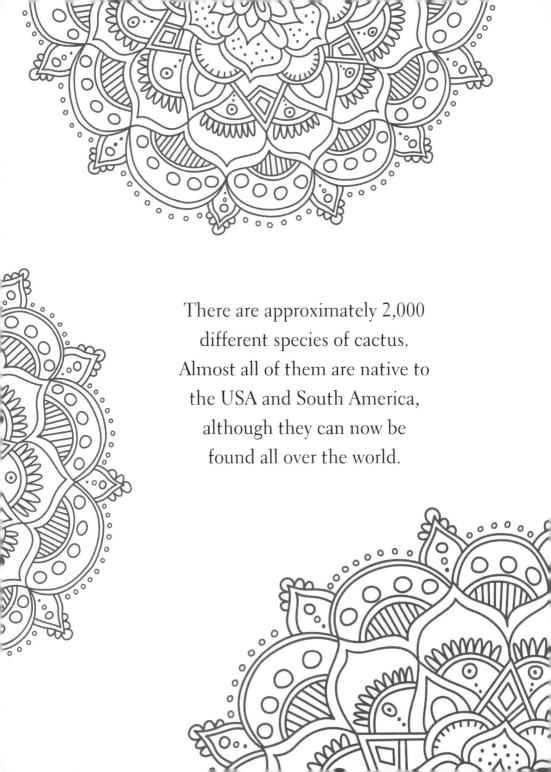

There are approximately 2,000 different species of cactus. Almost all of them are native to the USA and South America, although they can now be found all over the world.

Cacti aren't just spiky; they also bear flowers in a variety of colours: white, red, pink, yellow or violet and, like other flowers, cacti are pollinated by insects and hummingbirds.

Nearly all cacti are succulents:
the stems, roots and leaves all
store water for the plant so that it
can survive in drought conditions.
The spongy tissues of its flesh
force water down to the roots of
the plant to stop evaporation.

You can drink the liquid inside some cacti. It is thick and gooey but it has saved many lives in the desert. You have to be careful to select the right cactus – scratch the skin of an *Opuntia* cactus to release the liquid, or make a hole in the skin of a columnar cactus.

Cactus spines can be used
for sutures, after they have first
been sterilised on hot coals.

Cacti can be propagated via
seeds or stem cuttings. Use small
pots containing a mix of garden
soil, sand and fine gravel to plant
the seeds. Do not overwater.

Rebutia cacti from Bolivia and Argentina are just a few centimetres tall, although they have a large root.

The fruits of *Cereus repandus* from Peru do not bear prickles and are called cactus apples. Syrup can be made from cactus fruits.

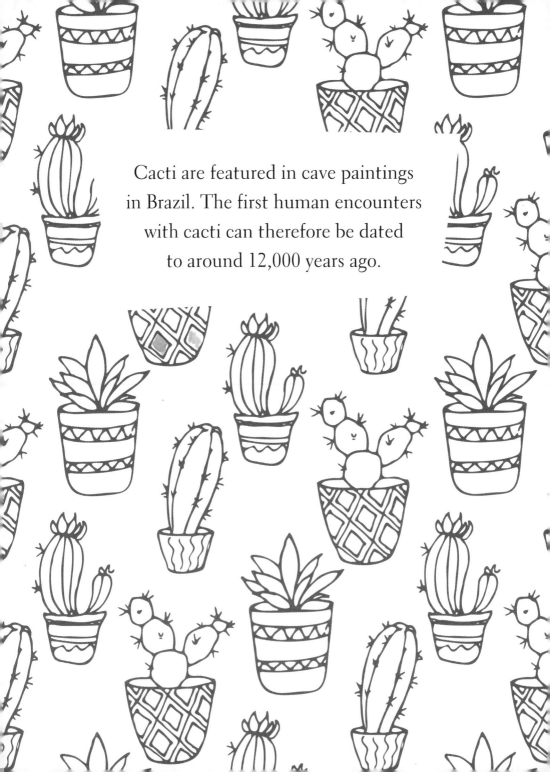

Cacti are featured in cave paintings
in Brazil. The first human encounters
with cacti can therefore be dated
to around 12,000 years ago.

Even small-sized cactus plants have
big roots, although they are not very deep,
usually not extending beyond
10 centimetres below the surface of the
ground. However, they often spread to wide
areas, covering almost 2 metres in diameter.

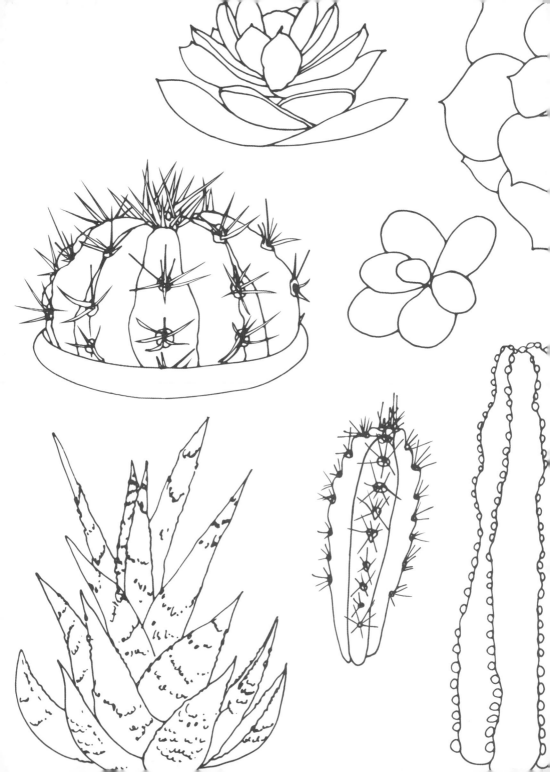

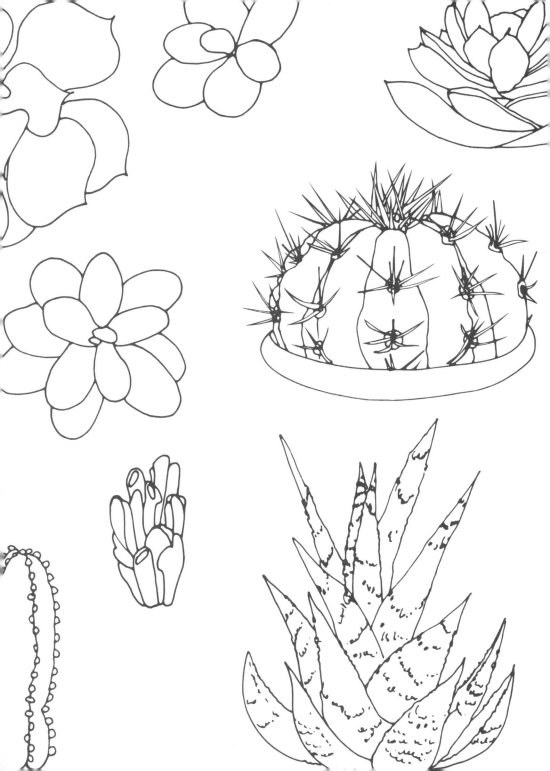

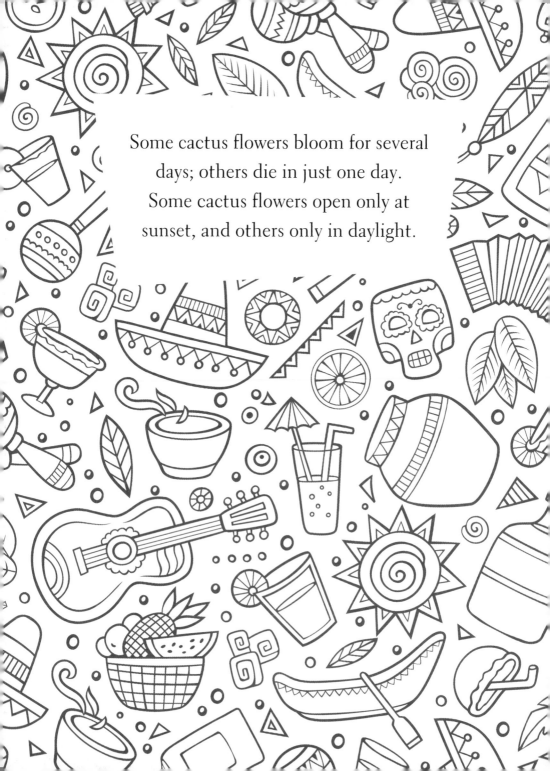

Some cactus flowers bloom for several days; others die in just one day. Some cactus flowers open only at sunset, and others only in daylight.

Beware the cactus. In 1982 an American man was killed after firing shots at a 9-metre-tall cactus. One of the cactus's limbs, having been weakened by the attack, fell on top of him, crushing him to death.

Cacti come in all shapes: some look
like chandeliers or columns, others are
flattened or oval and there are even
cacti that look like creatures such
as snakes, starfish or wild boars.

If you're interested in finding more about our products,
find us on Facebook at **Summersdale Publishers**
and follow us on Twitter at **@Summersdale.**

www.summersdale.com

Summersdale Publishers Ltd
46 West Street
Chichester
West Sussex
PO19 1RP
UK

www.summersdale.com

Printed and bound in the UK by Bell & Bain Ltd, Glasgow

ISBN: 978-1-909865-29-7

Substantial discounts on bulk quantities of Summersdale books are available to corporations, professional associations and other organisations. For details contact general enquiries: telephone: +44 (0) 1243 771107 or email: enquiries@summersdale.com.